Hands-on Science

An Introduction to the Bristol Exploratory

Richard Gregory

edited by Sonia Ashmore
with contributions by
James Dalgety & Francis Evans

Foreword by
Sir George Porter, PRS

Duckworth

First published in 1986 by
Gerald Duckworth & Co. Ltd.
The Old Piano Factory
43 Gloucester Crescent, London NW1

© 1986 by Richard Gregory

'On First Reading Einstein', first published in *Odd Perceptions*, essays by R.L.
Gregory (Methuen & Co Ltd 1986). Richard Gregory's reversible signature:
Scott Kim. Exhibition photographs: Martin Haswell. 'Underneath the Arches'
photographs: Steve Wragg. Line illustrations: Jonathan Newby. Pencil
drawings: John Williams (Wobbly Bridge, Light on Light, Elliptical Billiard
Table, Reflecting on Mirrors). Other diagrams: based on drawings by Avril
Jones. Captions: Richard Gregory and Priscilla Heard.

ISBN 0 7156 2136 X

British Library Cataloguing in Publication Data

Hands-on science: an introduction to the
  Exploratory at Bristol.
  1. Exploratory—Guide-books
  507'.4'02393   Q105.G72B7

ISBN 0-7156-2136-X

Photoset in North Wales by
Derek Doyle & Associates, Mold, Clwyd
Printed in Great Britain by
Ebenezer Baylis & Son Limited, Worcester

Foreword
Sir George Porter, PRS

The Bristol Exploratory is the brainchild of Richard Gregory and has come to fruition largely as a result of his enthusiasm. Almost everything that Richard Gregory does is a bit unusual, and the Exploratory is no exception – you will find nothing quite like it anywhere else in Britain and only one forerunner anywhere in the world. Here you won't find museum pieces or exhibits in glass cases; what you will find is so different that the Bristol Exploratory has added a new word to the English language: 'plores', which are, of course, things to be explored.

Most of us are born scientists, endowed with inquisitiveness and a strong desire to explore, to question, to discover. But many, perhaps most of us, lose our early enthusiasm for science when it becomes a formal subject, difficult and half understood, appearing to come *ex cathedra* from great minds of the past to whom we find it difficult to relate. But these great minds usually experimented and thought about things which were apparently very simple, similar to and in some cases identical with the experiments that you can not only see but *do* in the Exploratory.

Today we all live in a world of science, and to be ignorant of science is to be ignorant of a large part of life; it is like going through life without one of our senses. Such ignorance puts us among the 'hard of understanding' in most matters which concern twentieth-century men and women, as well as being a big handicap in finding interesting and rewarding employment. Such important bodies as the Royal Society, the Royal Institution and the British Association have recently become increasingly concerned about the public understanding of science and see the Exploratory as one of the most original British contributions towards improving this understanding.

This book gives a delicious foretaste of what is in store for those lucky enough to be in Bristol and able to visit its Exploratory. Most of us will be able, with a little thought, to solve some of the puzzles set for us here, but many are a real challenge even to professional scientists; in fact with a little hands-on experience at the Exploratory the young amateur may well get there before the professional and will certainly enjoy the game.

G.P.

Contents

Contributors

Sir George Porter, PRS
President of the Royal Society. President of the British Association for the Advancement of Science 1986. Nobel Prize Laureate for Chemistry 1967.

R.L. Gregory MA DSc FRSE
Scientific Director and Chairman of the Trustees, the Exploratory. Director of the Brain and Perception Laboratory and Professor of Neuropsychology in the University of Bristol

J.C. Dalgety
Project Director at the Exploratory

F.T. Evans MA
Principal Lecturer in the History of Technology at Sheffield City Polytechnic. Honorary Lecturer in the University of Sheffield

1. Bacon's New Atlantis

Richard Gregory

The Exploratory is designed to introduce and attract children and adults to Science and Technology. Its primary aim is to show us how naturally-occurring and man-made things around us work, and to help make us all familiar with the scientific way of asking and answering questions – instead of science appearing as incomprehensible claims and mumbo-jumbo methods as now it is for most of us. It should thus be a step towards melting the Snow dividing the Two Cultures: Art and Science.

Exploratory learning is not a luxury. A general understanding of science and technology is personally, and nationally, a necessity. As long as we remain clueless as to how our cars, TVs and refrigerators work – let alone the principles of atomic energy or guidance systems – we remain as children all our lives. Though this may be acceptable for a few years, while as children we are protected, lack of understanding leaves us vulnerable as adults, and it is hardly safe to give grown-up children the matches that science provides. Remarkably few people do appreciate, even vaguely, how the things around them work or why they sometimes misbehave, sometimes dangerously.

The aim of the Exploratory is to give people – both children and adults – world enough and time to experience interesting phenomena and carry out simple

NEW
ATLANTIS.

A Worke unfinished.

Written by the Right Honourable, FRANCIS,
Lord *Verulam*, *Vifcount* St. *Alban*.

MOTITI MELIORA

MEDIO FIRMA CRIA

Hon.ᵐᵒ Francisc.⁰ Bacon.⁰ Baro de Verulam. Vice-Comes S.ᶜᵗⁱ Albani. Mortuus 9 Aprilis,
Anno Dñi 1626 Annoᵩ Ætat 66.

experiments for themselves. The Exploratory is not, however, an alternative to schools, for it makes no attempt to provide systematic courses. Where written descriptions or explanations are required they are as short and simple and clear as possible, to prevent our Explorers being (as King John put it) 'bethumped by words'. Nor is it a museum, for it has only a few old or precious objects that must be protected from damage. It is a try-it-yourself Science and Technology Centre, where there will be information and help available, but basically the idea is to avoid as far as possible the presence of teacher middle-men between us and phenomena, which often speak clearly for themselves. There is fun and games to appeal to children and adults – games with almost frictionless air pucks, mirrors which displace and rotate, an elliptical billiard table, and much more, including mathematical and other puzzles.

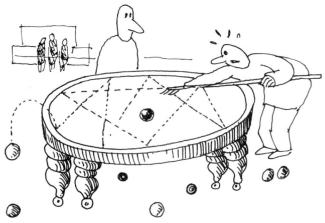

Snookered

How 'good' is a snooker table? Does it obey the simple laws of physics – of optics – that light comes off a mirror at the same angle that it strikes it? Is this strictly true for snooker or billiard balls? What about friction?

We have two snooker tables: one is elliptical. A ball placed at one focus should pass through the other focus from wherever it is hit. If it doesn't, spin, or friction or some other lack of 'perfection' has deviated it from its true path. The other table has various other curves (some of which are found in mirrors, for example in large telescopes).

In this attempt we stand at the feet, and hope to stand on the shoulders, of the late Dr Frank Oppenheimer, founder of the highly successful San Francisco Exploratorium Science Centre. There anyone who wishes can discover the properties of gyroscopes, light or magnets; a whole wealth of meaning-making experience is available. We essentially do the same here. We show how the products of technology work: how keys turn (or don't turn) locks, how TV pictures are built up from radio signals, what happens inside an electric motor or a fridge. We hope that people will appreciate technology more, and grow to feel more confident, and perhaps see new opportunities.

As the usual museum terms, such as 'exhibit', are too passive for the Exploratory's 'hands-on' approach, we have coined the word 'plore', meaning a model, an experiment, or a problem to *explore*. Coining some new words, appropriate to the aims, should help to reinforce the differences between the Exploratory and a Science Museum. Both, of course, have their place, and there is no competition or rivalry between them. As the Exploratory is not a custodian of historically important or valuable objects which need protection, we can dispense with glass cases. We are concerned with *principles* rather than with *things*. The plores, many of which are specially designed in-house, are the means for conveying principles of science and how these principles are applied in technology: for example pendulums in artificial gravity, illustrating how clocks work and what happens on the moon; or air bearings for almost frictionless machines such as gyroscopes — which are explored in many ways so that their strange forces can be experienced, literally at first hand.

Crazy Pendulum

This looks like an ordinary pendulum — but it swings wildly and unpredictably — because there are magnets below the bob. Often in science things are discovered by quite indirect effects, when they are invisible or cannot be detected by instruments. Here we gradually realise that there is something odd about this pendulum — such as hidden magnetic forces disturbing it. Pluto was discovered from observing surprising gravitational disturbances of planets, in this kind of way.

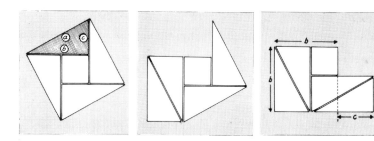

Proof of Pythagoras

We can see it is true from the wooden shapes. (Actually, this was appreciated by the Babylonians some 1500 years before Pythagoras – but he proved it, which was a great contribution of the Greeks.) Here we rely on seeing that a square area is equivalent to a square number. So we see (intuitively) that the square of the hypotenuse of a right angle triangle is equal to the sum of the squares of the other two sides. But intuitions are not always reliable!

The experiments and demonstrations start with human perception: with the explorer-visitor finding out how his senses provide information to perceive and understand – and sometimes misperceive and misunderstand. For, although the physical sciences aim for 'objective' knowledge by replacing, so far as possible, the human observer with instruments, ultimately it is our observations (even though sometimes via instruments) that convey our reality. So there is a wide range of perceptual experiments – on seeing, hearing, touch and the other senses. They look inwards at perceptual phenomena, to suggest by direct experience what is going on when we see or hear or otherwise perceive objects or events. These are insights into processes for experiencing and gaining knowledge. But astonishingly enough this is still hardly considered in schools, though

13

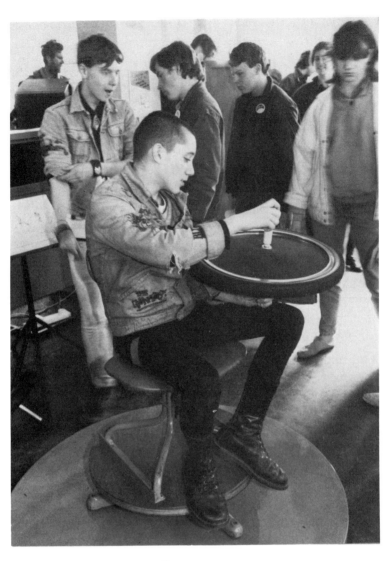

Gyroscopes

(i) When you spin the small bicycle wheel, and pick it up by its handles, then tilt it, you will feel the strange forces of gyroscope 'precession'. The bicycle wheel — which is a

gyroscope – resists your tilting force, and its axis rotates at right angles to what you might expect.

(ii) The large and much heavier bicycle wheel allows you to make this force effective. When you sit on the special chair, spin the gyroscope bicycle wheel, and tilt it, you will rotate on the chair! When you play with it you will experience some fundamental forces of physics.

all our knowledge depends on perception and exploratory interaction with the world of objects.

From perception and learning we move to the recording of muscle activity, looking non-invasively into the body at such vital functions as the beat of the heart. Then we move away from ourselves, to principles of mechanics and physics and how they are combined in technology. This ranges from simple (though fascinating) mechanisms, such as weighing scales or sewing machines, to the more hidden principles of the forces of nature, such as electricity and magnetism, and how computers work. Finally we reach Artificial Intelligence and Robots – to see ourselves through the eyes, and with the concepts, of technology.

The opportunity to try things out hands-on (rather than via the push buttons and glass cases of conventional science museums) allows our visitors – the Explorers – not only to appreciate phenomena and the way that moving models, mechanisms and so on work, but also to discover conditions under which they do *not* work – and so the *range* of conditions necessary for phenomena to occur or to make things work effectively. Examples are the building of catenary arches with bricks, and the

15

1. *Levitating ball. The jet of air keeps the ball levitating — even when the jet is far from vertical. It is remarkable how stable this is, as one finds out by trying it.*

2. Attracting balls. Here are two beach balls. When air is blown between them — what happens? You might expect them to move apart. But actually they come together. This is because the faster-flowing air, between them, has lower pressure. This is the basis of flight, for it is the reduced pressure at the upper surface of wings that holds aircraft up. Actually this follows from basic physics — but it is surprising.

testing of the Bernoulli effect of blown air to produce suction in some conditions. By active trying out and playing, optimal conditions may soon be discovered and tested – which is the basis of the learning of any skill. For contrast, imagine trying to learn how to ride a bicycle in a glass case, by passively watching it and pushing buttons!

By optimising conditions for making things happen, we learn how carefully or well something needs to be done, and what can be left to inattention or chance. This is important, for saving time and effort by restricting attention to where it is most needed frees the attention in a well-learned skill, for noting (and perhaps going on to explore) alternatives – even occasionally for inventing something new, or a new way of doing it.

Together with these 'insights' on perception we

introduce physiological principles of perception and learning. Linking these two approaches are perceptual illusions. These are fascinating phenomena and well worth considering, for though they may look trivial, as illusions of the senses are departures from physics, they are wonderful windows for seeing and coming to understand some of the subtle processes of perception. Examples are errors of size and distance and shape; errors of movement from alternating flashing lights (an illusion that makes the cinema and television possible); errors of ghostly non-existent shapes (which may indeed make people believe they have seen a ghost); impossible – paradoxical – pictures and actual three-dimensional models which should not, but do, exist. Then there are moving 3-D shadows, and a 3-D drawing machine for (not possible with paper and pencil) drawing or doodling in depth.

At the Exploratory there is an atmosphere of good humour and tolerance, combined with an element of challenge. Young animals and children learn by *play*, so it is strange that many educationalists still think of play as a trivial activity. In the Exploratory many of the 'plores' for exploring are fun, as games are fun. Many indeed can *be* games: games played with friends and, as science is, games played against nature. There is a place here also for some jokes; for jokes are surprising juxtapositions that jolt the mind: hollow faces, for instance, that look normal – until rotated, when they move in the wrong direction; the 'disappearing leprechaun'; a shape that exactly fits a circular, a square and a triangular hole. The Exploratory experience will, we hope, enrich our everyday perception by providing encounters with surprises. Some plores attract particular

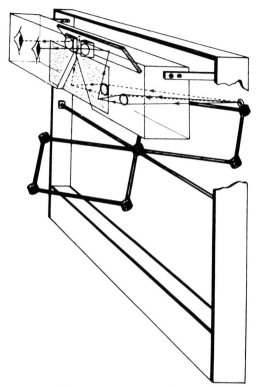

3-D Drawing Machine

Try drawing a knot in three dimensions. It is impossible, even for the greatest artist with pencil and paper — but you can do it with this device.

It works by projecting slightly different views of a moving drawing light on to electroluminant panels, which store the images as they are created by the moving light. When it moves in or out the pictures are slightly different — signalling stereoscopic depth. (This was invented by Richard Gregory).

attention because they are surprising. For example, blowing air between the suspended balls of a Bernoulli demonstration is surprising, in the right kind of way, since most people expect the balls to *separate*, instead of coming together into the air stream. By playing around with the jet of air it is easy to discover the range and limits of the phenomenon. The practical importance of this curious effect can be demonstrated in the lift of the upper surface of aircraft wings. Such failed predictions signal gaps of understanding or intuition, which can make us miss highly significant facts and ideas; and by learning to appreciate our failed predictions we may discover crucially important gaps in our understanding. There should not be too many dramatic surprises, however, or the Exploratory will be confusing. It is reassuring to get things right. Some initial hypotheses should therefore be confirmed!

Several of the plores reveal hidden features of the world, especially ones that cannot normally be sensed. This is done quite simply: for example, by magnetic fields made visible with iron filings, or pressure-waves of sound made visible with the gas flames of a Rubin Tube. More interactively, inertial forces are demonstrated by the handling of a spinning gyroscope wheel that allows surprising forces, which are usually hidden, to be experienced literally at first hand. The entire point, indeed, of technologies such as radio and television is to make audible or visible features of the world which are normally beyond the limits of sensory experience. By starting with human perception, these technologies, and how and why they work, take on an immediately human significance.

Not all the Exploratory plores will be completely understood, at least at first acquaintance. Much of

Three Kinds of 3-D Picture

Pairs of photographs taken from slightly different positions can give 3-D depth. This is because our eyes have slightly different pictures (retinal images), as they are separated — and the brain combines their two views to give stereoscopic depth perception. There are various ways of presenting stereo pairs of pictures to see them in 3-D.

The most familiar are 'stereo pairs', seen one with each eye with an instrument — a stereoscope — or with red-green glasses.

'Lenticular' pictures do not need any special instruments. They have many vertical cylindrical lenses — so that each eye sees a different picture, printed behind them, in alternate strips.

Holograms were invented in 1947 by Dennis Gabor. He invented them sixteen years before the invention of the laser — but they need laser light to photograph them, to be effective. Holograms are interference patterns and are entirely different from ordinary photographs.

To see these in 3-D you should come to the Exploratory!

Hidden Magnetic Force

*It is well known that iron filings make visible magnetic fields.
But are there, really, lines of force when there are no filings?
This is curious: the filings line up in individual lines in a
continuous force field. So they can be misleading. But there
are other ways of showing what the hidden forces are like.*

science and technology is essentially hard to understand,
even for experts. A plore that is not fully understood is
not necessarily inappropriate, however, for it is absurd
that we should expect to understand everything fully at
first acquaintance; some plores indeed raise questions to
which no one has a complete answer. But setting up
interesting questions may help people to enjoy *living by
questioning*, which can be stimulating and exciting.
Puzzling plores, especially when they intrigue and
please the Explorer, may help to reduce the surely far
too common fear of questions and imbue confidence. It

is an important point that plores that puzzle may be simple and familiar, such as the mirror-reversal plores and, far more profound, Newton's Bucket. How many people realise that what happens to the curved surface of the water in the spinning bucket poses the fundamental question of Absolute or Relative motion? With both these examples, it is important to make the context and the problem clear, without being intimidating. We have a lot to learn if we are to do this well, and any advice, criticism and help from our visiting Explorers will be appreciated.

Seeing Sound – the Rubin Tube

The flames respond to air pressure, so we see a 'standing wave', or many other phenomena of pressure changes in the air, by the heights of the flames.

Plores are grouped and related to reveal principles or generalisations which may be difficult to show directly.

For example, models of conic sections, and elliptical and parabolic billiard tables, show properties of nature which underlie the motions of planets and the optics of telescope mirrors. While each cut cone is individually evocative, together they allow us to appreciate significant principles. Thus examples of resonance show a general principle, which applies to a vast range of phenomena and to many technologies – from clocks, through electrical phenomena and musical instruments and the mechanisms of hearing to the fundamental dynamics of matter as seen in chemistry. This extension of perception by interacting and playing with forces of physics and seeing how they are applied in technology is essential to the aim and strategy of the Exploratory.

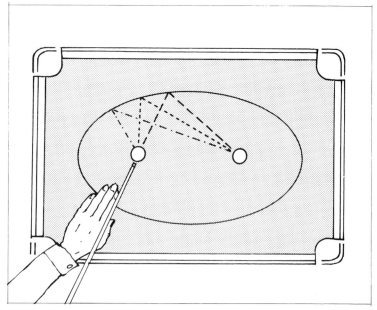

Some plores show how physical principles are combined in novel ways as inventions in technology, to produce (generally, though unfortunately not always)

desired results. Where results are undesirable, it may turn out that the new problems can be solved by applying science with further technology. These may, indeed, be spurs to invention rather than grounds for pessimism.

Although history is not the main aim of the Exploratory, to get a feel for the processes of invention it is essential to have some historical sense. We generally think of museums as Time Capsules, protecting precious objects of the past from damage, or up-dating, by their glass cases. In the Exploratory time-travelling can be far more rewarding than simply looking at old things, for here we can touch and use and play and experiment with the kinds of tools and toys that were familiar in the past. We can measure the speed of sound as Newton did by clapping his hands to the echo, or measure the speed of light, and nerve impulses, with the increasing accuracy of new techniques and instruments, as they were in turn invented. This, as the past is re-lived, will bring out clearly and dramatically the intimate relation with science and the mutual gains of all manner of techniques, tools and instruments. For example, we can carry out Galileo's experiments with weights rolling down inclined planes, first with the eye-ear-hand methods for observing and timing their fall available in Galileo's and Bacon's seventeenth century, and then with modern instruments. So here, by our own experiences and difficulties, we may come to appreciate what past science and technology were like – and how we have advanced and may now move further on with our technology. There is no obvious limit to this link from the past to the present – to anticipate and invent our future with creative intelligence – guided by understanding science and technology. The Exploratory should help to create an exciting future in which more of us can share and be effective.

Our aim to provide working demonstrations and experiments to allow people to explore principles of science and discover how things work for themselves is no new idea, however, for just this was conceived in the seventeenth century by Francis Bacon in his fascinating fragment of a book *The New Atlantis*, which appeared in 1667, the year after his death, though it failed to have the impact of his *Novum Organum* of 1620, which inspired the founding of the Royal Society.

Bacon's New Atlantis is an imaginary country containing the fabulous 'House of Salomon' – an Exploratory Science Centre. Bacon supposed that it was founded before the classical Greek philosophy which he disliked so much for its logic-chopping and, as he saw it, lack of observation and experiment for discovering pure and useful truths. The House of Salomon is his alternative. It contained the engines of technology as well as the instruments of science. It was designed for pleasure, to stimulate and amuse, as well as for finding out about the natural and man-made world, and human capabilities and limitations. What Bacon described three and a half centuries ago, is the essence of our Exploratory. Thus there are

> ... perspective-houses, where we make demonstrations of all lights and radiations; and of all colours; and out of things uncoloured and transparent, we can represent unto you all several colours; not in rainbows, as it is in gems and prisms, but of themselves single. We represent all multiplications of light, which we carry to great distance, and make so sharp

as to discern small points and lines; also all colorations of light: all delusions and deceits of the sight, in figures, magnitudes, motions, colours: all demonstrations of shadows. We find also divers means, yet unknown to you, of producing of light originally from diverse bodies. We procure means for seeing objects afar off; as in the heaven and remoter places; and represent things near as afar off, and things afar off as near; making feigned distances. We have also helps for sight, far above spectacles and glasses in use ... We make artificial rainbows, haloes, and circles about light. We represent all manner of reflexions, refractions, and multiplications of visual beams of objects ...

We have also sound-houses, where we practise and demonstrate all sounds and their generation. We have harmonies which you have not, of quarter-sounds, and lesser slides of sounds ... We represent and imitate all articulate sounds and letters, and the voices of and notes of beasts and birds. We have certain helps which set to the ear do further the hearing greatly ... We have also means to convey sounds in trunks and pipes, in strange lines and distances.

We have also engine houses – Also fire works for pleasure and use. We imitate also flights of birds; we have some degrees of lying in the air; we have ships and boats for going under water, and brooking of seas; also swimming-girdles and supporters. We have divers curious clocks, and other like motions of return, and some perpetual motions. We imitate also motions of living creatures, by images of men, beasts, birds, fishes, and serpents ...

We have also a mathematical house, where are represented all instruments, as well of geometry as astronomy, exquisitely made.

We have also houses of deceits of the senses; where we represent all manner of feats of juggling, false apparations, impostures, and illusions; and their fallacies. And surely you will easily believe that we have so many things truly natural which induce admiration, could in a world of particulars deceive the senses, if we would disguise those things and labour to make them seem more miraculous.

27

Oppenheimer's Exploratorium in San Francisco, founded nearly twenty years ago, is indeed Bacon's dream come true: an enchanted palace where anyone can by his own initiative discover what science shows and how it works and also, perhaps, why it sometimes fails to come up with the goods. The Exploratorium has thriving daughters in several American cities, and Oppenheimer's ideas have immense impact in the Museum and Science Centre world. It is surprising that the significance of this enterprise has taken so long to reach Britain, though the Human Biology Exhibition at the Natural History Museum in London, and now the interactive Launch Pad Gallery in the London Science Museum are impressive examples of this move towards Hands-on Science.

The importance of active exploration – and the inhibiting effect of glass cases – was impressed upon me over twenty years ago when, with my colleague Jean Wallace, I studied the case of S.B. Sidney Bradford was effectively blind from early infancy, with opacity of the corneas of both eyes. One day, after more than fifty years of blindness, he received corneal grafts. To our astonishment we found that immediately after the first operation he could see some things immediately, without having to learn; though some other things took him months or years to see. It turned out that he could at once see things he already knew from his earlier exploring of the world by touch. Most dramatically, he could immediately tell the time by sight, since years before he had learned to read time by feeling the hands of his pocket watch, from which the glass had been removed. Even more surprising, he could immediately read upper-case, but not lower-case, letters. It turned

NEW ATLANTIS

WEE failed from *Peru*, (where we had continued by the fpace of one whole yeare) for *China* and *Iapan*, by the South Sea ; taking with us Victuals for twelve Moneths ; And had good Winds from the Eaft, though foft and weake, for five Moneths fpace and more. But then the Wind came about, and fetled in the Weft for many dayes, fo as we could make little or no way, and were fometimes in purpofe to turne backe. But then againe there arofe Strong and Great winds from the South, with a Point Faft ; which carryed us up, (for all that we could doe) towards the North : By which time our Victuals failed us, though we had made good fpare of them. So that finding our felves, in the Midft of the greateft Wilderneffe of waters in the world, without Victuall, wee gave our Selves for loft Men, and prepared for death. Yet wee did lift up our Hearts and Voices to G o d above, *who fheweth his Wonders in the Deepe* ; Befeeching him of his Mercy, that as in the *Beginning* Hee difcovered the *Face* of the *Deepe*, and brought forth *Drie-Land* : So he would now difcover Land to us, that we might not perifh. And it came to paffe, that the next day about Evening, wee faw within a Kenning before us, towards the North, as it were thicke-Clouds, which did put us in fome hope of Land : Knowing how that part of the South-Sea was utterly unknowne : And might have Iflands or Continents, that hitherto were not come to light. Wherefore we bent our courfe thither, where we faw the appearance of Land, all that night : And in the Dawning of the next Day, wee might plainely difcerne that it was a Land Flat to our fight, and full of Bofcage : which made it fhew the more Darke. And after an Houre and a halfes Sayling, we en-

tred

out that he had learned upper-case by touch when a boy at the Blind School from letters engraved on wooden blocks. The blind children were given only upper-case letters, since lower-case was not used at that time for street signs or brass plates which it would be useful to read by touching. So the Blind School inadvertently provided us with just the needed controlled experiment! It told us that active exploration is vital for seeing – which indeed is the basis for the Exploratory.

Most moving, and most informative to us, was S.B.'s reaction on first seeing a lathe. He loved tools, and for years he had wished he could use a lathe. Shortly after he left hospital we showed him a simple lathe in a glass case at the Science Museum in South Kensington. Then, with the help of the museum staff, we opened the case to let him touch it. As reported at the time (Gregory and Wallace 1963, p.33):

> We led him to the glass case, which was closed, and asked him to tell us what was in it. He was quite unable to say anything about it, except that he thought the nearest part was a handle. (He pointed to the handle of the transverse feed.) He complained that he could not see the cutting edge, or the metal being worked, or anything else about it, and appeared rather agitated. We then asked a Museum Attendant for the case to be opened, and S.B. was allowed to touch the lathe. The result was startling; he ran his hands deftly over the machine, touching first the transverse feed handle and confidently naming it as a 'handle', and then on to the saddle, the bed and the head-stock of the lathe. He ran his hands eagerly over the lathe, with his eyes shut. Then he stood back a little and opened his eyes and said: 'Now I've felt it I can see.'

This is just one item of the evidence that perception

depends on 'reading' or interpreting sensory signals in terms of knowledge – or in terms of assumptions, which may be wrong – of the world of objects. There is an absolute dependence upon active exploration for learning to read the neural signals from the eyes and the other senses, and generally for understanding. This is such a general principle that it is an axiom of Artificial Intelligence – which we hope to explore as this is a most exciting future science.

There are, though, some dissident authorities who do not think this way. Thus the American philosopher John Searle has claimed quite recently (1980), and still maintains, that no man-made computer can ever even in principle understand the meanings of symbols. Since the issue is so fundamental to the notion of the Exploratory, let us consider it further. Searle offers the analogy of Chinese handing Chinese symbols or characters to a Westerner in a closed room. The Westerner knows no Chinese. He learns to recognise the Chinese characters, and he may anticipate which will be needed from sequences and so on, and so be able to help the Chinese by passing characters as needed, but he will never come to understand the meanings of the Chinese symbols. According to Searle, this is the plight of computers: they can handle symbols usefully but they can never ever understand them. This blind handling of symbols that cannot be understood is, for Searle, an essential limitation of all future man-made computers, though (curiously, as there is no clear reason why machines should be essentially different here from organisms) he allows that an unknown Martian might understand symbols, though a computer could not. We might well ask: Could a child, brought up in the conditions of Searle's Chinese Room, do any better than the adult Westerner? How indeed could the Chinese themselves have learned the meanings of their symbols as children if they had been brought up in Searle's closed room? Surely the point is that, for any kind of reading or seeing or understanding to be possible, there must be a window to the room. Or better, there must be at least a stick to probe the world outside for an eye to see, or a mind (or computer) to understand. We follow Francis Bacon in thinking that such issues are probably not for philosophers to decide, though their questions and analyses can be extremely useful, for these issues need to be explored by trying and testing with experiments. Looking into the future, we will indeed explore such issues as these – as we travel from our own perception, through physiology, physics and other Natural Sciences – to human intelligence encapsulated in technology. We hold not only that technology is the result of human imagination and understanding, but also that the techniques and working principles of the machines and instruments of technology have always been the main basis and inspiration of science and philosophy.

However this may turn out, the Exploratory is primarily intended to capture people's imagination. It does not have to be as thorough or 'complete' as a school or a University; so topics and plores can be chosen to evoke interest and stimulate curiosity without the necessity for a complete course or a comprehensive account. The Exploratory should be a useful resource for schools, and help teachers. Explorers are encouraged to fill their gaps by thinking for themselves, and seeking further information or deeper explanations.

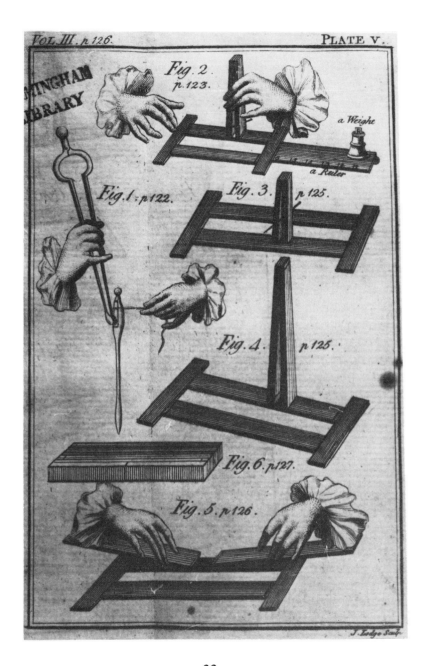

Fig. 2.
p. 123.

a Weight

Fig. 1. p. 122.   *Fig. 3.*   *p. 125.*

a Ruler

Fig. 4.   *p. 125.*

Fig. 6. p. 127.

Fig. 5. p. 126.

33

The games in the Exploratory are no new idea either. In 1783, for instance, there appeared a book in four volumes, with hundreds of plates, by a W. Hooper with the splendid title: *RATIONAL RECREATIONS, in which the Principles of NUMBERS and NATURAL PHILOSOPHY are clearly and copiously elucidated, by a series of EASY, ENTERTAINING, INTERESTING EXPERIMENTS. Among which are All those Commonly performed with the Cards.* This showed pre-Victorian children how to understand, by making things and experimenting, and by fun and games. This game-like quality may indeed be part of the fascination of computers for children today. We do not however want everything to be simulated in the Exploratory. It is important to play around with actual pendulums and clocks and prisms; and actually to measure the speed of light to meet and become friends with science.

The Exploratory is not like school, as it need not be constrained by the needs of exams, but it should be an effective educational resource, which offers experience and knowledge in some ways beyond the range that schools can provide, and it can be far more exciting as an experience. To achieve these aims the Exploratory must itself explore new ideas, and technologies for teaching and learning and presenting information. The Exploratory must appeal to anyone whose curiosity might be stirred to appreciate how things tick, or enjoy reasonably rational recreations.

Should you think that these ideas are upside down, try turning the book around.

Richard L Gregory

References

Francis Bacon: The Advancement of Learning and New Atlantis, edited by Arthur Johnston (Oxford 1974), pp. 243-6.

R.L. Gregory & Jean G. Wallace, *Recovery from Early Blindness: a case study*. Quarterly Journal of Experimental Psychology monograph no. 2 (1963), reprinted in R.L. Gregory, *Concepts and Mechanisms of Perception* (London 1974), pp. 65-129.

R.L. Gregory, *Mind in Science* (London/New York 1981).

John R. Searle, 'Minds, brains and programs', *The Behavioral and Brain Sciences* 3 (1980), 417-57.

2. On First Reading Einstein

Richard Gregory

Believe it or not, I first read Einstein's wonderful book *The Theory of Relativity* in the library of the *Queen Elizabeth* – in 1943, in the middle of the war, when she was a troop ship. This crossing to America, in mid-winter, was not entirely uneventful. There was a violent storm, and several of the ship's boats were smashed by the waves breaking over her decks. Some of our chaps were injured on the companion ways, for the ends of the ship moved sickeningly up and down, over some fifty feet, so that we were alternately immensely heavy and almost weightless. The ship carried a large gun on her stern which may have had some effect and she was driving through the gale at top speed. We were up all one night fully dressed as we zig-zagged through a German ambush of six submarines, while a running commentary from the tannoy system told us what was happening. It was while all this was going on that I discovered Einstein.

Here in this little book of a hundred pages – through the pitching and rolling, with the unnatural listing first to port and a few minutes later to starboard as we made yet another torpedo-defeating turn, with the wild noise of wind and wave, orchestrated by running feet and occasional shouted orders as a background to the world torn apart by war – here in this little book was distilled intense imagination controlled with a perfect precision of art. Starting from 'the noble building of Euclid's geometry', I was transported with accounts of moving railway carriages, and people ascending in lifts, to considerations of space and time that were beyond experience, though based on very simple observations. The storm and the submarines and the orders faded away, 'till the dawn broke on a troubled sea'.

Although each sentence is crystal clear, Einstein's book is extremely *difficult*. It is difficult because to understand it requires deep perceptual re-learning. We have to come to see and experience the forces in familiar moving carriages and lifts and ships differently. We have to journey impossibly, as when Einstein travels through space at the speed of light looking for his face in his shaving mirror. Will he see his own face? Will light allow it? Wonderful that the speed of light turns out to be an ultimate limitation. I still feel dizzy when I think of it.

As children, we discover the world hands-on (and not just hands-on, for we bite things too and learn from the responses of others) so how we see is probably very largely by what we have been able to explore. This in part is why we see many things quite wrongly – such as the sun and stars moving to the west, though it is we that are carried to the east by the rotating earth. It is amusing that Aristotle thought that the earth must be stationary because, when he jumped straight up, he landed where he took off – which of course couldn't happen if the earth was rushing under his feet while he left it. This was 'of course' for Aristotle (and I assume also for today's children) because he did not have our concept of inertia. Aristotle regarded the continuing movement of a missile as due to air moving in to push it along from behind. Now that we understand inertia we

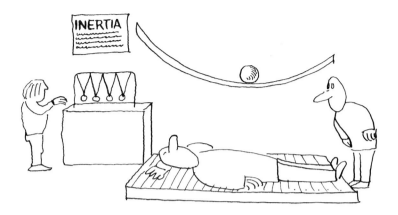

reverse the 'of course' to: 'Of course we keep moving with the earth when we jump because of our momentum, which is the inertia of moving things – so what's the problem?' For us now the concept of inertia, after the three hundred or so years since Galileo and Newton, is a reference – a kind of context for seeing motion and understanding the forces on ourselves as we are accelerated in pitching ships or whatever.

Then we read Einstein's little book – and bang goes this reference in our mind. For the comfortable concept of inertia turns out to be related to the mean mass of the Universe – as, in a way, Newton found with his lovely water-in-a-spinning-bucket experiment. Newton saw that when a bucket of water, suspended on a rope, spins round, the water at first remains flat; then, as it takes up the spin of the bucket, its surface becomes curved. If the bucket's spin is suddenly stopped, the water's surface remains curved, until it comes to rest with respect to the bucket and the room – or rather the Universe. When the bucket is set to spin, before the water catches up with it the water remains flat, so its motion with reference to the bucket is irrelevant: all that matters is

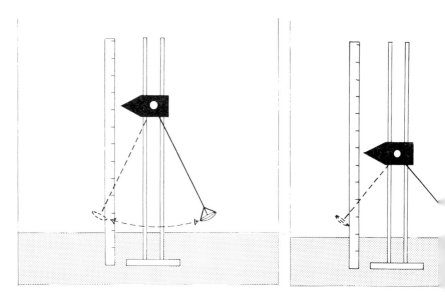

The Swing of Things

Galileo realised that a pendulum swings for (almost) the same time-period with a small or a large swing. Thus he invented the pendulum clock. The mass of the bob does not matter; but as the length is increased the period lengthens, by the square root of the length of the pendulum. This plore pendulum is self-maintained, electro-magnetically.

In the Exploratory, you can check the Laws of the Pendulum for yourself, by changing the length of the string, the weight of the bob, and the amplitude of the swing. (The time of each swing is recorded on an electronic counter.)

What happens to pendulums up mountains – or on the Moon – where gravity is weaker? They are slower! Although the mass of the bob has no effect (a pendulum with a heavy or light bob swinging at the same rate) the gravitational pull under it is important. A pendulum on the Moon, or up on a mountain on Earth, swings slower. And a pendulum on a massive planet

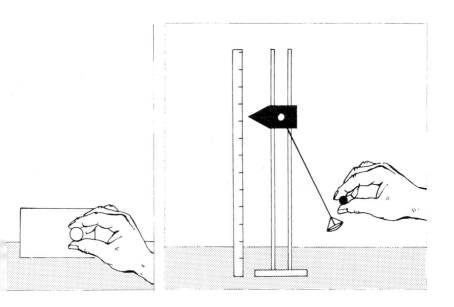

such as Jupiter would swing faster. *We show this with magnets – to give artificial gravity changes – so we can space travel to the Moon or to Jupiter with a pendulum. (This is not altogether a cheat, as it does genuinely change the restoring force on the pendulum's bob, much like a gravity change.)*

(For the significance of this, see above: On First Reading Einstein.*)*

its motion against the rest of the Universe. But what if the bucket weighed as much as, or more than, the Universe of stars? Would the bucket experiment give the same result? Following Ernst Mach and Einstein, we can see that it would turn out quite differently. Although the step is beyond observation or experiment, we can imagine it, and we see the result, given these changed concepts of inertia. Or is this 'seeing'?

41

Einstein was puzzled that inertial mass is *exactly related* to gravitational force. Could it be just an incredible coincidence? Or are they ultimately the *same*? Suddenly inertia doesn't look at all simple – yet it might be a key to finding deep simple accounts of how things are.

Pendulums are beautiful. It is wonderful that the swing of a free pendulum keeps in the same direction in space, so that we can see the earth rotating under it. One day I was playing with pendulums to make an experiment for the Exploratory. I was comparing what happens when the *length* of the string, or the *weight* of the bob, are changed. The shorter the string, the faster the pendulum swings, but if the bob is made *heavier*, or *lighter*, there is *no* change in the rate of swing. This is remarkable because a heavier bob is attracted more strongly to the centre of the earth, so the restoring force is greater – and it should therefore swing faster. It does swing faster in a stronger gravitational field, and slower in a weaker gravity, as on a mountain, or on the moon. Indeed – and this was the point of the Exploratory experiment – if the bob is a magnet, attracted to a long strip magnet beneath it (which is really only possible with recently available magnets), the pendulum swings faster, though it is in a fixed place on Earth. And a repelling strip magnet placed beneath it slows the swing, as though it is on the moon. So one can do a kind of space-travelling with pendulums. But, as a pendulum swings faster with stronger gravitational (or magnetic) pull, why doesn't a *heavier* bob swing faster than a light bob? The reason is that the increased *inertia* of the heavier bob requires more force to accelerate it, and the extra force required is *exactly* the increased gravitational attraction. This means that inertia and gravity are precisely related. For Newton this exact relationship was a total mystery. It was too much of a coincidence, and yet there was no visible or conceptual link between inertia and gravity to explain it.

This was one of the questions that led Einstein to suppose that inertia and gravity are ultimately the same. But to say this he had to re-describe and re-see the Universe – and then persuade his fellow physicists to follow him, which they did. So, much hangs on a pendulum.

We have to be switched into an exploratory mode by such questions to move away from our infant learning and childish view to see the Universe as it is described by physics. Then everything looks very odd. It is odd not only because so much of it lies outside our 'immediate' experience, whatever that is, but also because familiar things become related in different ways. Given significant questions, playing with pendulums and other quite simple toys and phenomena allows us to re-live our original perceptual-conceptual learning, to open our eyes and understanding for new perceptions. Given good questions, playing with a pendulum can be more effective for knowledge-gaining than the most expensive and powerful tools. This, at least, is the hope of Hands-On Science.

This is part of what I learned, that stormy wartime night, at peace with Albert Einstein.

Reference

Albert Einsten, *Relativity. The Special & General Theory. A Popular Exposition*, translated by Robert W. Lawson (London 1920).

3. Underneath the Arches

Francis Evans

In just one way engineers have an easier problem in space than on earth. Orbiting objects are weightless, and therefore they do not have to be designed to carry their own weight or the weight of people and things inside them. In space, a solar collector which is kilometres square is feasible; under earth conditions it would buckle like newspaper. We are surrounded by structures which carry loads: things like tables, aeroplane wings, shelves, legs (living and otherwise) and bridges. Even plants and trees have to stand up under their own weight.

Gravity is a force. Usually we think of a force as making things move – bowstrings push arrows, we let go of a plate and gravity pulls it down to smash on the floor. But gravity is still pulling that plate when it has landed on the floor – the force has not disappeared. So a force can be at work even though it is not moving anything! What happens sounds odd. The floor pushes back against the plate.

You can see this better when you put a weight on a plank. The plank is pushing back with a force equal to the weight. If the weight were stronger, the plank would give way and eventually break. If the plank pushed harder than the weight, the weight would rise up in the air. But how can a floor or a plank push? The answer is that they are *strained* – bending them stores energy in them. Take the weight off the plank and it springs back – it gives back its energy.

This storing and giving back of energy is more obvious in rubber bands, or in a bow. You apply a force, and the band stretches, the bow bends. Let go, and *twang* – the stored energy is given back, quickly. Now *everything* behaves like that, less obviously. A big bridge is designed to be so stiff that you don't notice it bending, but it does. The biggest, strongest bridge in the world bends very slightly if a fly lands on it. Engineers like stiff materials for their structures. They use brick, concrete, steel, iron and wood – not rubber. Even so there are big variations in the way that these stiff strong materials behave. Think of a material which is strong if you *pull* it but not if you *push*. Ropes, wires, chains and cables are all like this. They are strong in tension, but not in compression. You can't push a rope.

Similarly, some materials are strong in compression, in crushing, but not in tension. Stone or brick, for instance, are very strong when weight rests on them, but are brittle and come apart when they are pulled. Brick walls stand up because of the weight of the bricks pushing down from above. It is weight, not cement, that holds them together and that is why walls are built so carefully not to lean.

Some materials are good both in tension *and* compression. Wood is a good example. If you want to know how strong a material is, you have to test it. We stretch, crush, twist and hit materials in machines, and measure their behaviour.

BUSTER

This *buster* is a simple way of doing compression and tensile tests on samples you can cut out for yourself. Unlike the very precise laboratory machines, it does not need specially made test pieces; samples cut out of tin cans, plastic cartons or bits of copper wire will do.

If the tests are done slowly they are more interesting. With the *buster* you can measure how much force it takes to break a sample and see how much it stretches before breaking. You can find out whether it just snaps or stretches and 'necks down' before it fractures, and you can begin to have an idea of what materials are strong or weak, brittle or ductile, treacherous or trustworthy.

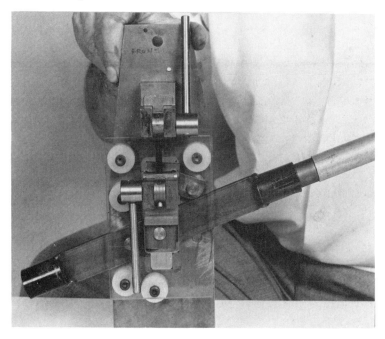

THE BEAM

The simplest way to carry a load across a space is on a beam. If you put weights on this model beam and watch the water in the tubes, you will see the water go up in one and down in another and stay the same in the middle one. Why? The answer is that the top is getting shorter (compressed) and the bottom is longer (in tension) – so the water moves in the tubes.

Wood and steel are good for beams because they are strong in both *tension* and *compression*. But there are things that you cannot make beams out of: brick, stone and cast iron. These are brittle materials – and break at the bottom where the beam is stretched most. So how can you make a bridge if you want to use materials that are only strong in compression?

THE RAINBOW ARCH

These arches are for playing with! You can put them together to see how strong they are. If one end block is lifted a few centimetres you can feel how the arch is *pushing*. That is the thrust of the arch: with a weight placed on top, it pushes even harder.

Anything that pushes has to push *somewhere* – it has to have a direction. In these arches it is not straight down, but more sideways. So the downwards force of the blocks and the weight is turned outwards by the arch and carried into the side supports. There is no glue or chewing gum holding these blocks together. Nor is anything *pulling*. The arch is a *push* structure, pure compression.

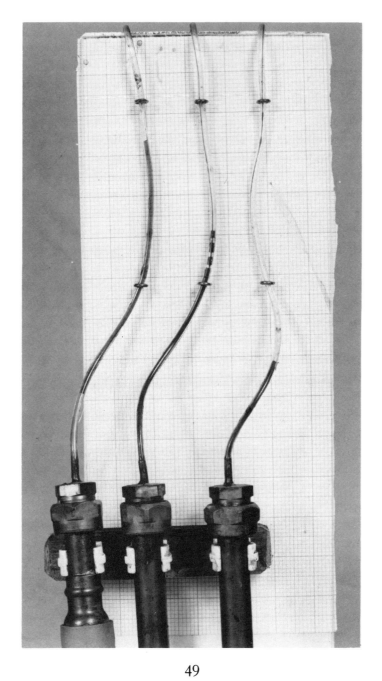

49

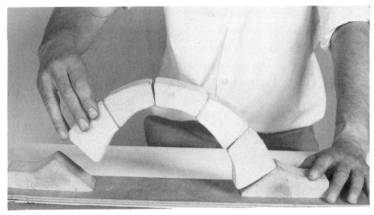

50

51

THE WOBBLY ARCH

Arches push, and pushes don't just go anywhere – they have to go in some particular direction. The arch wobbles like a jelly which shows this point. The blocks are curved, and this means they only touch at one place. That one point of contact *has* to be where the thrust is – if it were pushing against nothing, it would move. So any block in the arch is being kept up by the push from the blocks on either side – and you can say that it is pushing them back.

The arch rolls into other shapes if you put different loads on it (try it with the small weights) and the line of thrust changes too. The curved strips will fit the thrust line where the blocks touch.

When the arch has gone a long way out of shape, the line of thrust gets close to the edge. Push down a bit harder, and the line of thrust goes outside the arch and it collapses – the blocks cannot contain it any more. They pivot at the corners, as if they were on a hinge. Real arches fail like that – not because the stone is crushed and broken, but because the weight in one place is too heavy for its thrust to stay inside the stone.

The Romans and Normans built arches for thousands of years without really thinking this out. Robert Hooke worked out the principle of arches about 300 years ago. He left his solution to posterity in the form of a Latin anagram, *Ut pendet continuum flexile, sic stabit contiguum rigidum inversum*: 'An arch stands as a loaded chain hangs.'

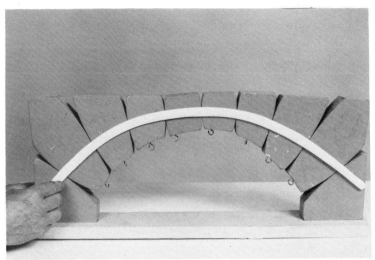

The 'Wobbly Bridge' shows the forces passing through the bricks or stones in an arch. (This take-apart-build-for-yourself model was designed by Francis Evans).

On this model you can notice the shape of the chain when the wobbly arch blocks are hung from it. With a weight hung from a different point, the chain will take a new shape which can be compared with the shape of the arch's line of thrust.

The arch and the chain are the same, but there is one big difference. The chain is in tension (remember you can only pull a chain), but the arch is in compression.

THE SUSPENSION BRIDGE

The chain has a graceful curve where the forces of the bridge run. They change direction as each vertical string adds the weight of a bit of deck to the chain. Chains are strong but they are not stiff, and they shape themselves to the forces on them. If weights are put on this bridge the chain changes shape, to follow the changing forces on it. Real arches cannot change shape like that, so they have to be thick enough to let the different lines of thrust run through them.

Soldiers are ordered to break step when they march across suspension bridges to avoid a strong rhythmic vibration. If you put your finger on this bridge and press ... and press ... and press ... you will soon find the rhythm that the bridge snakes to. If marching feet hit that rhythm on a real bridge the snaking builds up until there is an almighty crack.

The wind can do it too, setting up a flutter in the bridge. Little bridges have little flutters, big ones can whip up and down as much as ten metres – unless the deck is designed to let the air flow smoothly over it.

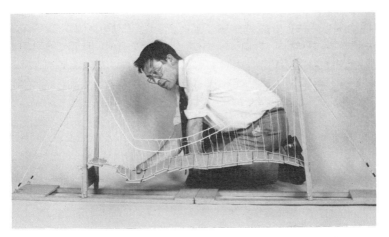

FLAT CHAINS AND FALLEN ARCHES

Suspension bridges have high towers and deeply plunging chains although it is usually cheaper to build low.

You can feel the reason for yourself if two people hold a cord with a small weight hanging from it. Stand close to one another and guess how much weight each of you is holding. Now move apart and feel the force growing in the cord. Pull with all your might – many, many times more than the force of the little weight – and the cord will still sag. It would take an infinite force to make that cord perfectly straight.

You don't have flat arches for the same reason that you don't have flat chains on suspension bridges – the flatter the arch, the more the force pushes sideways. The flat arch needs weight on the trapeze at the end even to stand up at all. If you try different weights on the bridge you can see what weight you need to hold the abutments in.

Higher arches are not really so fussy – this can be seen with the round arch and the Gothic arch. The Gothic arch is especially unwilling to push outwards. Those old masons who built the great cathedrals were not stupid, even if they did not know about Hooke and his chain.

THE FLYING BUTTRESS

Early medieval buildings with vaulted roofs had thick walls and small windows to stop the arches pushing the wall over. You can feel with your hand how easily a little pressure on the arch pushes the upright column over. If you fit the flying buttress you can feel how much stronger the structure becomes. The flying buttress took the thrust down to the ground, so that the walls and pillars of the cathedrals only carried small vertical loads. This is why the glorious Gothic cathedrals have such great windows and slender pillars.

THE RIDDLE OF THE FOUR HINGES

Here's a funny thing: you can push your finger down on the arch and count how many cracks appear in the joints. All arches except one make the same number of hinged cracks as they open up. There is one arch where it is a different number – the flat one. Flat arches cannot fail by hingeing as the curved ones do because the thrust line cannot get out of the shape. They would be the best sort of arch if it were not for that enormous thrust at the abutments.

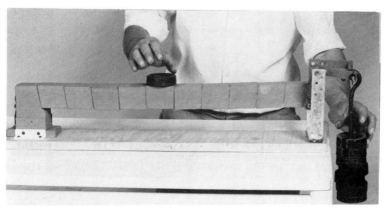

Except for the *Catenary Arch*, the models which you can play with at the Exploratory are copyright prototypes made by Francis Evans.

References

J.E. Gordon, *The New Science of Strong Materials* (Penguin,1973).

J.E. Gordon, *Structures, or Why Things Don't Fall Down* (Penguin, 1978).

Derrick Beckett, *Bridges* (Hamlyn, 1969).

H.J. Hopkins, *A Span of Bridges* (David and Charles, 1970).

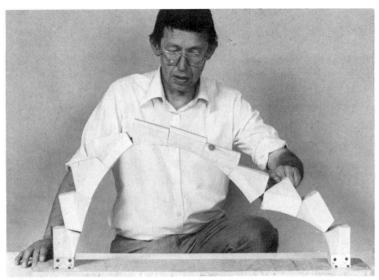

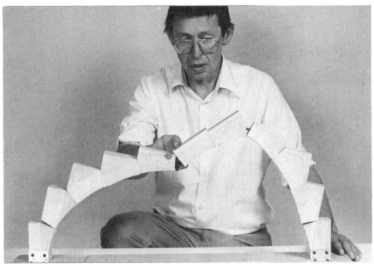

Contract Bridges

Why do bridges (usually) stay up? Some are in compression (arches), others in tension (suspension bridges). Both follow, when not loaded, the same curve — the catenary.

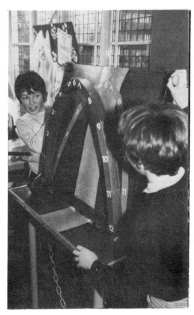

Impossible Triangle

This odd object looks impossible, from a critical viewing position. When the two ends line up the eye — or rather the perceptual system of the brain — assumes that they lie in one plane. This false assumption generates a paradoxical perception.

4. Puzzles

James Dalgety

The earliest history of puzzling is full of deceit, death, cheating and generally unsporting behaviour. Riddles seem to have been very popular BC.

In the Bible Samson asked the Philistines his famous riddle: 'Out of the eater came forth meat, and out of the strong came forth sweetness' (Puzzle 1). By modern standards this would be considered a swindle. Perhaps it has lost something in translation. Whiston's 1784 translation of Josephus' *Antiquities of the Jews* quotes the riddle thus: 'That a great devourer produced sweet food out of itself, though itself were very disagreeable.' I confess to being not very excited by either version. However, the Philistines became really worked up and got riddling off to a good start by threatening Samson's wife, Delilah, who tricked her husband into revealing the answer. This started one of the earlier Middle Eastern Wars, in which she and her father were burnt, thousands were slain with an ass's jawbone, and so on.

Hiram, King of Tyre, used to send 'sophisms and enigmatical sayings' to King Solomon and desired that he would 'solve them and free them from the ambiguity that was in them'. Solomon must have been handy at riddles, for Josephus describes him as 'so sagacious and understanding that none of these problems were too hard for him, but he conquered them all by his reasonings'. They used to gamble large sums on riddles, and Hiram used to lose badly until he employed one Abdemon of Tyre to help him out. The riddles have not survived, but cheating has.

In Greek mythology the Sphinx used to ask young men, 'What walks on four feet in the morning, on two at midday, and on three in the evening?' (Puzzle 2). Again the stakes were high – if you got the wrong answer you got eaten. When the young Oedipus eventually gave the right answer the Sphinx committed suicide, and Oedipus went on to kill his father, marry his mother, and have a generally depressing time.

Homer is reputed to have died of frustration at being unable to answer the fisherman's riddle: 'What we caught we threw away, what we could not catch we kept.' (Puzzle 3).

During the Dark Ages riddles must have flourished, as by 900 AD they had been enlivened with sexual ambiguity to throw one off the track and elaborated with references to the words and letters of which the riddles themselves were constructed. Some were delightfully silly:

A creature walked among wise men
sitting in crowded assembly;
it had one eye and two ears
and two feet and twelve hundred heads,
back and belly and two hands,
arms and shoulders, one neck
and two sides. Say what I'm called.
(Puzzle 4)

Something of the art of the riddle has been lost in this century. 'Why did the chicken cross the road?' (Puzzle 5), hardly compares with:

Can you tell me why a hypocrite's eye
Can better descry than you or I
On how many toes a pussy cat goes?
(Puzzle 6)

or

How many bears make a proverb?
(Puzzle 7)

Of course everyone knows that, when the riddle is in verse, so should your answer be.

63

The trouble with riddles is that like crossword clues and rebus picture-puzzles they can be considered 'unfair' as they rely on special, often culturally exclusive, knowledge. 'Proper' puzzles contain all that is required for their solution within themselves and so transcend cultural and language barriers. One of the earliest topological puzzles was devised by Gordius, a king in Asia Minor. He tied the yoke of his wagon to a pole outside his palace with a knot of bark. After many years it was believed that whoever undid it would become ruler of all Asia. Many tried and failed until Alexander the Great came passing by in 333 BC, drew his sword and cut the Gordian knot, and thus became another of the world's great cheats, which is perhaps why he never did conquer all Asia.

After the fall of Jotapat (67 AD), Josephus, our aforementioned historian, is reputed to have been holed up in a cave with 40 other survivors who were so scared of the Romans outside that they decided to commit suicide. Josephus and one friend didn't fancy the idea at all but thought they should appear to agree, so Josephus said they must do it in an orderly fashion: they should arrange themselves in a circle and then count around clockwise killing every third person until the last person left could commit suicide. Can you work out where he placed himself and his friend so that they could cheat death? (Puzzle 8).

In 181 AD, Hung Min, a Chinese warrior, is supposed to have invented the Chinese Rings puzzle to keep his wife occupied while he was away at the wars. The Chinese Rings have been used as a simple lock, and are related to the fabled 'Tower of Hanoi' or 'Brahma Pyramid':

Beneath the dome in the Temple of Benares which marks the centre of the world, may be seen Three Diamond Needles set in a base of Brass. On the first of these Needles there were placed at the Creation of the world 64 Discs of Gold of diminishing sizes. Since

that time the priests have been employed without
intermission day or night transferring the discs one at
a time (no larger disc resting on a smaller one); and
when according to the unchangeable laws of Brahma,
all the 64 discs have been rebuilt in their proper order
on the third Needle, the whole world will crumble
away.

Assuming that this puzzle does exist, can you work out
how accurate the prophecy is? (Puzzle 9)

To solve your own Brahma puzzle, lay out playing cards as indicated, then move the stack one card at a time onto the third ace, never putting a higher denomination on a smaller (Puzzle 10). Using aces instead of diamond needles and 12 playing cards instead of 64 gold discs will be found much quicker and cheaper and I hope won't stop the world. Can you spot the relationship of these puzzles to modern electronic computers?

Puzzles exploit the deficiencies in the way we have been taught to think and the way we have learnt to perceive things. This is why they are an essential part of the Exploratory. Try to balance six nails on the head of a seventh (Puzzle 11). This is a very simple problem. There are no tricks or catches, so why do most people find it difficult?

Can you guess what the following description is about?

The puzzle was sold by the million and for a short time almost monopolised the attention of Europe and America. Huge prizes were offered for a correct solution, and the world positively 'went mad' over this little thing. And it has been stated, though doubtless with Yankee exaggeration, that some 1500 weak-minded persons in America alone were driven to insanity by it. Certain London shops in Cheapside and elsewhere sold nothing else and were besieged from morning to night, while hawkers at every street corner found it impossible to supply the demand.

Does this sound an apt description of the Rubik's Cube craze of 1981? It is in fact a description of the Fifteen's puzzle craze of 100 years earlier. If you can solve Rubik's Cube it is probably only because you learnt

somebody else's solution when the cube was the centre of that crazy craze a few years ago, whereas you can probably do the Fifteen's puzzle instantly (Puzzle 12). Slide the blocks into numerical order without lifting them.

The general state of understanding was such that the Fifteen's puzzle was as difficult to comprehend in the 1870s as Rubik's Cube is to us today. Will our grandchildren have developed to the point that they have an instinctive understanding of Rubik's Cube puzzles and fail to comprehend our difficulties?

Most people think only of jigsaws, crosswords or Rubik's Cubes when the word 'puzzle' is mentioned.

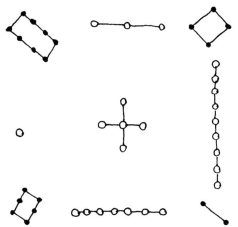

There are hundreds of other types, however. Mazes have a long history rooted in mythology and mysticsm. The first magic squares were given to the Chinese engineer-emperor Yu the Great by a miraculous dragon-horse and a turtle before the fifth century BC. (The exact date is a puzzle.) Puzzle drinking-vessels which have to be drunk from without spilling have been around for centuries. Puzzle locks, boxes, jewellery, pocket knives, nails – you name it, and it has probably been made as a puzzle at some time.

Try some of these more or less well-known puzzles.

If you and I want to share a cake and be absolutely fair, obviously one of us cuts it and the other chooses who will have each half. Can you think of a fair way for any other number of people to share a cake (or perhaps to avoid crumbs, a stew)?

As a trainee electrician you are given some wire, two identical heating elements, one on/off switch, and one two-way switch. Can you wire them into a simple heater with off, high, medium, and low temperature settings? Is this a puzzle or just an elementary exercise? (Ron Cook of Pentangle devised this puzzle).

You have a pair of scales (but no weights). You have 12 coins, one of which is a forgery weighing either more or less than the others. Can you always identify which one it is, and whether it is heavier or lighter than the rest, in only 3 weighings?

Three teachers, only one of whom can row, and three schoolchildren, all of whom can row, have to cross a river in a boat which will only hold two people. In order to avoid being given homework there must never be more teachers than pupils at any time on either river bank. How do the children manage this?

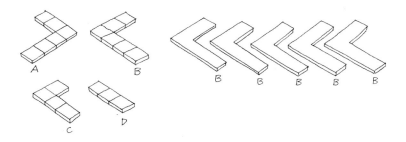

Cut out these pieces of cardboard and assemble them into a square. You must not turn the pieces over.

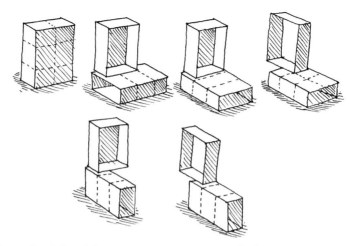

Oscar's Matchboxes were invented by Oscar Van Deventer from Holland. All you need is five standard matchboxes (side ratios of about 3:2:1). Make the five pieces by glueing outsides to insides as illustrated. The puzzle is then 'simply' to close all five boxes without twisting or damaging them in any way. There are several solutions.

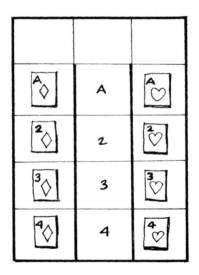

How did you get on with the Tower of Bramah? Try this improved version. Mark out and number, in all three columns, a diagram as illustrated on a large sheet of paper, with the rectangles big enough for playing cards. Place the Ace, 2, 3, 4 of Diamonds on the right and Ace, 2, 3, 4 of Spades on the left. The puzzle is then to swop the Spade and Diamond columns by sliding the cards around on the diagram. Not more than one card on a rectangle and no card is allowed to cross a thick line, move diagonally, or rest on a number higher than itself.

ANSWERS

Puzzle 1: Honey from the corpse of a lion. (Judges 14:4).
Puzzle 2: Man
Puzzle 3: Fleas
Puzzle 4: A one-eyed garlic seller
Puzzle 5: Depending on your age and background: 'To get to the other side', 'For some Fowl reason', 'To see Evelyn Laye'.
Puzzle 6: 'A man of deceit can best counterfeit,
And so I suppose, he can best count her toes.'
Puzzle 7: 'Bear and Forbear: Obviously five bears'.
Puzzle 8: 31st and 16th.
Puzzle 9: Not very accurate at all. Allowing one second per move 2^{64} = 18,446,744,073,709,551,615 moves/60 seconds/60 minutes/24 hours/365 days? = 5,849,424,173,000 years. The anticipated remaining life of the earth is 3,500,000,000 years. It has already been going for four and a half billion years.

If you want more answers, come to the Exploratory where you will also find more puzzles – including where leprechauns disappear to and how to fit square pegs into round holes.

Radiating Lines Distortion

The vertical bars are illusory – and so is their curvature. The figure is actually just radiating lines with gaps, across which the illusory bars appear, and – just as for actual lines – they are distorted, to appear curved.

5. Exploring the Plores

After-Images in the Eye

Stare at the picture, then look at blank paper, or the wall. The picture appears – in reverse – like a photographic negative. Your eyes (actually the retinas at the back of the eyes) store the picture for a few seconds, much like a fading photograph.

This could explain many ghosts. The after image of a large keyhole – or a candle flame – looks like just a nun, hovering around the room!

A Dishy Illusion

Are they the same size? Try cutting out pieces of card like these, and move them around. You can make the small one larger – and of so course the larger one smaller.

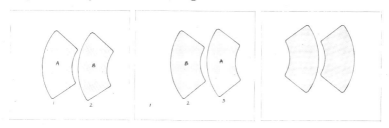

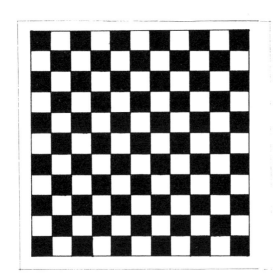
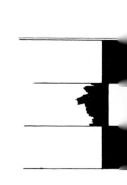

The Cafe Wall

This is named from seeing these dramatic wedge distortions in the tiles of a nineteenth-century cafe, at the bottom of St. Michael's Hill in Bristol. How can an essentially symmetrical

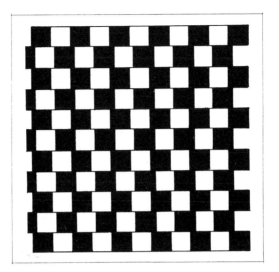

pattern produce these large asymmetrical wedges? They reverse when alternate rows of the squares ('tiles') are shifted by one square width.

This effect is unusual for distortion illusions, for it depends on brightness differences of the tiles. The horizontal 'mortar' lines must be narrow, and brighter than the dark tiles and darker than the light tiles for the distortion to occur strongly.

Perspective Shadows

What is perspective? The small source of light produces sharp shadows of anything placed between the light and the screen. The shadow, for example of your hand, will halve in size with each doubling of its distance from the light. So the wire models look distorted – the parts nearest the light looking too large. But this is exactly the 'distortion' that the images in the eyes have, whenever you see objects at various distances. It is also the 'distortion' that artists use to represent distance in pictures – for artists draw distant objects smaller. Although these shadows *are precise perspective pictures – and correspond exactly with the pictures in the eye – perspective is usually reduced in perception, by what is called 'Size Constancy' scaling.*

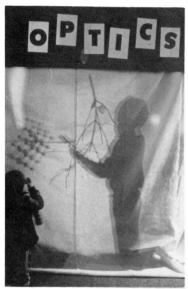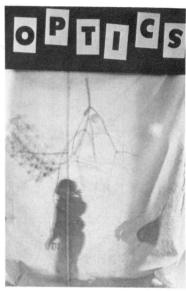

3-D Shadows

This is exactly like the Perspective Shadows – except that here we have two perspective shadows, one for each eye. The brain combines the slightly different viewpoints to give 3-D perception from an object, or model, which in the Exploratory you can hold and move around. Try it!

The Skeleton Cube that Shows the Bones of Perception

The skeleton cube sometimes appears 'correct' – then it will spontaneously flip in depth; so that the back appears to be the front. Then it reverses its direction of rotation, and it appears distorted. Its apparently further face looks too big. (This is because the apparently further but actually nearer face is enlarged, by perceptual 'Size Constancy', which normally

78

makes objects at different distances correct in size. But here it produces distortion as the depth is reversed — so the Constancy Scaling works backwards, to produce this distortion).

Bacon's Telephone

Early in the seventeenth century Francis Bacon described how it is possible to talk over long distances by putting sounds through tubes.

Chladni Plates

When a brass plate, covered in fine sand, is stroked with a violin bow it vibrates — making a loud sound. The sand forms beautiful patterns, corresponding to the regions of the plate which are in violent motion ('Nodes') and parts which remain stationary ('Antinodes'). Where they are depends mainly on the shape of the plate and where the bow strokes it. (*The waves cannot ever get shorter than the distance between the atoms of the metal!*)

The House of Light Rays

A point-source of light, with some vertical slots in front, allows us to see the effects of mirrors and prisms and lenses — how they reflect, deviate, refract and focus light.

Ears on Tubes

When the funnels on the ends of the tubes are moved around — your ears effectively move with them. You can cross them over — then someone speaking to you from the left will sound from your right.

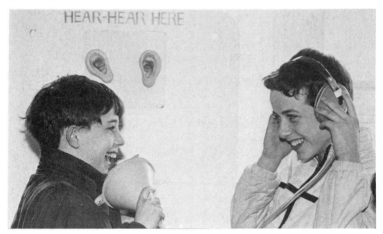

Louder Speakers

Loud speakers have vibrating cones to move as much air as possible to convey sounds to the ear. In this 'plore' we try not just cones but anything to hand – from an ashtray to a dustbin. Roughly – the bigger the better – the dustbin is much louder.

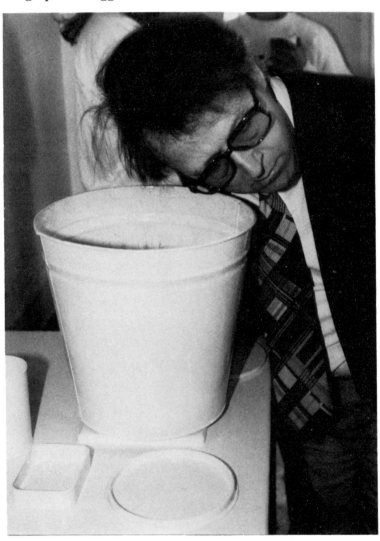

Seeing Sounds

An oscilloscope (which is rather like a TV set) allows us to see any electrical change. A microphone produces electrical changes – so we can see sounds. We can see the complex air-pressure changes of our voices, of a tuning fork (a simple sine wave) or any sound however complicated. A high note (such as a whistle) gives more waves on the screen – but what one sees also depends on how the instrument is adjusted. One really needs to play with it to understand how it works and what it can show.

It is amazing that the most complicated sounds – of many voices and a whole orchestra of musical instruments – can be seen as a single wave on the oscilloscope screen – and can be reproduced by the single motions of a loudspeaker cone.

3-D Pendulum – The Pulfrich Effect

Looking at the swinging pendulum, or the rotating wheel, through a dark glass placed over one eye, with both eyes open – the pendulum seems to move in an elliptical path though in fact its path is straight. The wheel appears tilted.

The eye viewing through dark glass sees the pendulum slightly in the past — *and so in a different position (except when the bob is stationary at the ends of the swing) from the other eye. This horizontal difference of signalled position gives* stereoscopic *depth signals to the brain. The delay is because the dark-adapted eye accepts (integrates) light over a longer period — like a longer camera exposure — for dim light.*

See at a Glance

Here is a new game. The problem is to hit the target with the ball bearings — with one, two, or three or more mirrors. The 'perfect' law is that the angle that the ball hits the mirror (actually the rubber strip under it) equals the angle of reflection. This is strictly true for light — is it true for balls? Accept the challenge of one, two, or more mirrors — and place them anywhere you like, and select the angles at which you think the balls will hit the target. Then give it a go. Hold a ball at the top of the shoot, let it go, and see what happens. Does it hit the target?

84

By looking down at the 45 degree mirror on the shoot, you can see the pure perfect solution that light adopts. Does the ball behave as perfectly? As Milton put it, does it hit the target equally, 'With thy long levell'd rule of streaming light'?

Aereal Puck

How can we reduce the annoying irrelevancies of friction – to show the perfection of Newton's Laws of Motion? Air gives a virtually frictionless passage to the puck – which bounces from magnetic springs. This is about as close as one can get to the simple perfection of the frictionless motion of the planets, which allowed Newton to describe the Universe from his first Law: A body will remain at rest or will move at constant speed in a straight line, unless it is perturbed by external forces. Play with the airborne puck and shake hands with Newton.

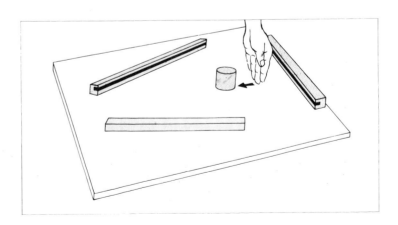

Throwing Light on Light

Some Bulbs Grow — This One Disappears!

The parabolic mirror (from a wartime search light) gives a real image of the actual bulb — producing a powerful optical (not a perceptual) illusion. You might get a shock if you try to touch the bulb in the Exploratory.

Focussing Heat

Radiant heat is just like light, except that it has a lower frequency or longer wavelength. Here heat is imaged by optical mirors.

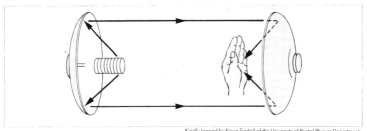

Kindly loaned by Kevin Tindall of the University of Bristol Physics Department

Drawing Evocative Curves

The ellipse can be drawn with a length of string and two pins.
The cycloid is drawn with a pencil on a rim of a rolling wheel.

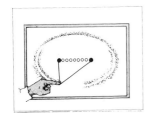

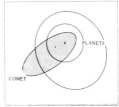

Convection Currents

A small electric heating element in a glass water bath sets up convection currents — which can be seen as moving patterns projected on to a screen — as there is a small change in the refractive index. The heated water is less dense — and so rises.

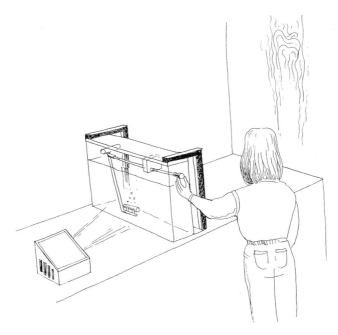

Cycloid Races

On the graph-paper wall are a cycloid curve (the path of a point on the rim of a rolling wheel) and a straight track. When a toy car is released from the top of the cycloid — it reaches the end at the same time as an identical car released from, say, half way down. They arrive at the bottom at the same moment! This is a remarkable property of a cycloid curve.

Just as amazing: the cars (or balls or whatever) reach the end sooner *than a race down the* straight *track — through the same fall. So, a straight line is not always the shortest distance between two points! (This is a basis of Einstein's account of space as curved).*

Reflecting on Mirrors

Why does writing reflected from a looking glass look right-left reversed — mirror writing? This looking glass can be rotated — but this has no effect, for it is symmetrical. Why, then, is the reflection reversed horizontally but not vertically?

When the pair of mirrors forming a corner is rotated — the image is rotated (at twice the speed of the mirror rotation) and the 'mirror reversal' can be avoided — so writing looks normal, and you look as others see you. (This is due to simple geometric optics.) But does this explain the left-right reversal of the single plane mirror? No — it doesn't!

Why does the plane mirror apparently reverse right to left, but not up to down? Is this optics? Is it reversed by the perceptual brain? Is it because you have two eyes, horizontally separated?

It is none of these. If you can't think of the answer an Exploratory 'pilot' might set you on course. (It is amazing how many people have sunk on this one.)

Hands-on Electricity

When different metal rods are held by the hands a small electrical potential is set up, from the acid of the skin. Electrons are drawn from one metal to the other – which registers as a small electric current on a sensitive meter.

Mirror Drawing

Drawing or writing in a mirror is extremely difficult – for what one sees does not tie up normally with how one's hand

moves. *Practice improves, though, and interestingly practice with one hand can improve performance with the other hand — so we must have a brain after all!*

Soap Solutions

Films of soap adopt minimal potential energy surfaces. Wire models with soap films show mathematical solutions which are very difficult to compute — but given immediately by bubbles. (This puts those clever mathematicians in their place!)

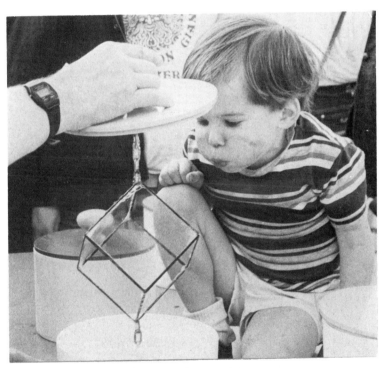

Bubble-film Projector

A soap film projected on a screen shows lovely colours (due to diffraction, or interference of light by its closely spaced surfaces) and various moving patterns as it loses molecules by drying.

93

Seeing Stress

Polarisation of light can be used to show stress in structures made of Perspex. The stressed regions show up as bands of coloured light.

94

Explorer's Pullover

With a block (a nautical pulley) a bloke, or girl, can tackle any weight. For each doubling of weight there must be twice as much rope pulled. Then the girl can pull over the bloke with the block.

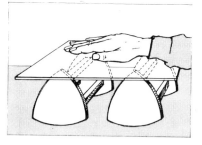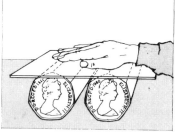

A Wheel that is not a Wheel

We are used to wheels running smoothly. We have shapes which are not circular and yet they have the same diameter for any rotation. This is true of a 50p coin – which is why it works in slot machines.

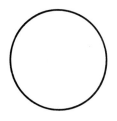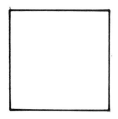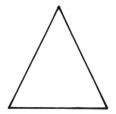

Circle, Square, Triangle Puzzle

Here is a board with a circular hole, a square hole, and a triangular hole. Note their sizes. Can you think of a single rigid solid object which would pass through the circle, the square, and the triangle – such that it will, in turn, exactly fill these holes? (The criterion is that no light will show when this special object is roughly half-way through a hole. And it must be able to pass straight through, so no flanges are allowed. The object may be made of wood or metal. What shape must it be?

It is none of these. If you can't think of the answer, come to the Exploratory and run a 'pilot' to ground – who might guide you through the shoals of your misunderstanding, to the truth.